Essential Food Hygiene

Dr R J Donaldson OBE Fourth Edition 2010

First edition 1988
Second edition 1993
Updated 1996 and 1998
Third edition 1999
Copyright (Text) © 1993-2002 Dr R J Donaldson, OBE
Updated 2002
Revised third edition 2006
Fourth edition 2010
ISBN 978 0 901619 16 7
© The Royal Society for Public Health

Introduction

In the first edition of this book, published in 1988, Dr R J (Paddy) Donaldson, wrote of food poisoning: "The danger lies in the ease with which it can strike: the cause is almost always human error. It does not happen by accident, but occurs when people store, handle, or prepare food incorrectly". Since then, there have been changes in the regulatory framework and the agencies responsible for food safety. This has seen changes in the food eaten, in the technology used in the preparation of food and in the way people buy and eat food. The future will bring further changes, including continuing growth in the consumption of ready meals and of meals outside of the home. There will also be larger numbers of older people whose meals will be provided for them either in their own homes or in care homes. Yet the truth of Paddy's statement has not changed. Food safety still depends on the people who store, handle or prepare food doing so correctly.

The purpose of this book is to enable anybody who works with food to understand what they need to do to ensure that the food is safe to eat. It is particularly relevant to people whose job involves working with food but it is also relevant to anybody who handles food at home and to young people who are learning about food.

Sadly, Paddy Donaldson passed away in 2005. The Royal Society for Public Health and many thousands of individuals have reason to be grateful for the clear and effective messages that he set out in *Essential Food Hygiene*. His legacy lives on in this newly updated edition.

Notes

Contents

A historical note

This section briefly outlines the history of our current understanding of food poisoning and points out that in spite of modern scientific knowledge, many mistakes are still made.

Early times

Concern about what food is edible and what food is not, has its origins in ancient times. Food poisoning as a disease has been recognised for centuries.

Bacteria: The key

During the second half of the nineteenth century, the scientific basis for the cause of many diseases, including food poisoning, became known when a famous French chemist demonstrated that bacteria could cause disease. At about the same time a German physician recognised that bacteria were responsible for a number of diseases, including cholera.

The dawning of this scientific era required a public education programme to inform people about the causes of disease and also to persuade reluctant government bodies to take action.

In these campaigns the Royal Society for Public Health took a leading role to promote health and improve the social conditions of the times. It was formed in 1876, and six years later Queen Victoria - who displayed great interest in the health of her people - became its patron.

The definitive link with bacteria as a cause of food poisoning came in 1888. A German doctor isolated bacteria from the organs of a man who had died in a food poisoning outbreak. He found identical bacteria in the left-over meat that the man and his companions had eaten as well as in the carcass from which the meat had come. It was gradually realised that food could be heavily contaminated with bacteria and yet smell and taste the same as normal food.

By the beginning of the last century food had become more plentiful and cheap, and the small eating houses of the day were often very unsanitary. At the time there were few reports of food poisoning outbreaks, possibly because of the small number of people involved. However, the more likely explanation is that the meat was cooked and served immediately to the customers, unlike the mass catering of today when food is cooked and held before serving sometimes, unfortunately, at the temperature at which bacteria can grow.

Many of the outbreaks of food poisoning today are caused when 'high risk' foods are held for too long within the Temperature Danger Zone (see page 14). Food safety is now a high profile issue with food premises being subjected to more regular inspections and, where necessary, to increased enforcement action by Environmental Health Practitioners.

Food poisoning

This section defines food hygiene and food poisoning, and provides the facts about the increasing number of reported food poisoning cases.

Food hygiene is the action taken to ensure that food is handled, stored, prepared and served in such a way, and under such conditions, as to prevent - as far as possible - the contamination of food.

Food poisoning can be broadly defined as those conditions caused by eating contaminated food or drink. The main symptoms are usually diarrhoea and/or vomiting, often accompanied by nausea (feeling sick) and stomach pains.

Food poisoning is weakening and extremely unpleasant, even for healthy people. However, when it affects **infants, pregnant women, elderly people and those with weakened immunity** (known as the 'at risk groups'), it can have serious consequences, and results in hundreds of deaths each year in the UK.

The onset of symptoms is usually sudden and may start within 2 hours of eating the food, but it can also begin after an interval of many days.

The illness typically lasts 1 or 2 days but sometimes can continue for a week or more.

The incidence of food poisoning

The total number of new cases is called the incidence of food poisoning. The number of cases in official statistics depends on people going to their doctor, who may or may not pass on the information for all cases.

In 2007, the Health Protection Agency (HPA) estimated the actual number of cases of food borne illness to be 926,000, with 18,900 hospitalisations and 440 deaths. In the same year, the Food Standards Agency (FSA) estimated the annual cost of resource and welfare losses due to food poisoning to be £1.5 billion, with 8 million working days lost annually.

Food poisoning cases have been falling steadily since 2000. This is probably due to recent reductions in cases of *Salmonella* due to the vaccination of hens in the UK, as well as improved hygiene standards. The major cause of bacterial food poisoning is now due to *Campylobacter*.

Trend in food-related illnesses in the UK: Recorded cases

Food Poisoning Notifications - England & Wales 1990 - 2009

Year	NOTIFICATIONS*		Total
	Formal	Otherwise Ascertained	
1990	36,945	15,200	52,145
1991	35,291	17,252	52,543
1992	42,551	20,796	63,347
1993	44,271	24,316	68,587
1994	50,412	31,421	81,833
1995	50,761	31,280	82,041
1996	50,718	32,515	83,233
1997	54,233	39,668	93,901
1998	53,764	40,168	93,932
1999	48,454	37,862	86,316
2000	46,481	40,047	86,528
2001	46,768	38,700	85,468
2002	38,541	34,108	72,649
2003	35,695	35,200	70,895
2004	34,376	35,935	70,311
2005	34,642	35,765	70,407
2006	32,800	37,803	70,603
2007	32,322	40,060	72,382
2008	29,023	39,939	68,962
2009+	29,795	45,197	74,992

* Includes Port health authorities   Source: Office of National Statistics (ONS)
Last update 24/02/2010   + provisional data

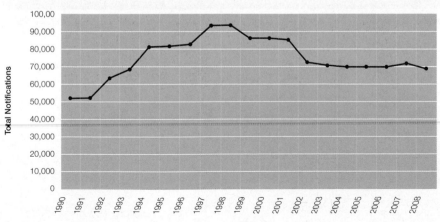

Care is needed in interpreting the increases of recorded cases. Outbreaks of food-related illness become high-profile media stories, which increases awareness not only among the public, but also among professionals. There is no doubt that this results in more cases being recorded. More people seek medical advice and more illnesses are notified by doctors. No one knows how much this accounts for increases. Most experts, however, accept that the overall increases, such as those seen in the UK between 1990 and 1998 are real.

The increase may have been due to:

- more intensive methods of rearing animals and contaminated animal feed
- breakdowns in temperature and hygiene controls in the distribution chain of convenience foods
- use of fewer preservatives
- lack of care in storage and preparation of chilled and frozen foods
- more eating out; poor standards in catering establishments
- better laboratory detection

In 2007/8 a UK survey was carried out by the FSA on fresh chicken in supermarkets which showed:

- 65% were contaminated with *Campylobacter* (76% in those of UK origin)
- More chilled chicken were contaminated (47%) than frozen (14%)
- *Campylobacter* was more often found in free range and organic reared than housed birds
- *Salmonella* in chicken at retail has remained low at 6.6%

Contamination of food

Contamination of food may create a hazard which can cause harm to a consumer.

A hazard may be:

Biological (for example, bacteria and their toxins, and viruses)

Bacteria are small living organisms - a colony of 25,000 could fit on the point of a needle. They are the most common cause of food poisoning in the UK.

Viruses are tiny particles - even smaller than bacteria - that can be identified only by using a special microscope. They only grow in living cells, and can't grow in food. Many of the measures that prevent contamination by bacteria also reduce the risk of viral infection.

Chemical (for example, chemical poisons and other poisons like insecticide)

Occasionally other poisons cause problems in food. Chemicals such as insecticides get into food, and toxic metal and cleaning fluids may enter food during processing. Some foods, e.g. dried kidney beans, contain a toxin which must be removed during preparation.

Physical (for example, undesirable substances in food)

Reports of 'foreign bodies' such as dead rodents, insects and plasters in food get wide publicity. Physical contaminants such as these are usually seen by the consumer and the food is not eaten. However, substances like glass can be dangerous as it is hard to see. These incidents rarely cause food poisoning.

Bacteria

This section describes bacteria as small living organisms that require food, moisture, warmth and time to grow.

The nature of bacteria

Bacteria are small living organisms often known as 'germs'. They are so small that it is impossible to see them without a microscope. Bacteria are usually round or rod-shaped.

Bacteria are everywhere:
in soil, dust, water, the air around us, and on our bodies.

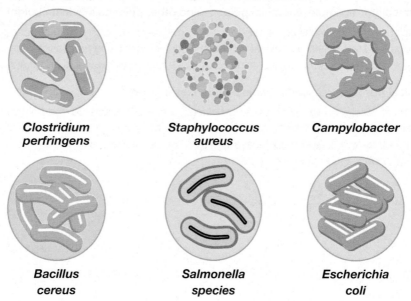

Clostridium perfringens

Staphylococcus aureus

Campylobacter

Bacillus cereus

Salmonella species

Escherichia coli

Most bacteria are harmless and some are even useful like those in our gut (intestines) that aid digestion. Certain bacteria are needed to manufacture products such as cheese and yoghurt.

Organisms that cause diseases are called **pathogens**. Normally, large numbers of most types of pathogens are required to cause illness, however exceptions are *Campylobacter* and toxin-producing *E.coli* that only need a small number of pathogens to cause illness.

Other types of bacteria can cause food to smell, to lose texture and flavour, and generally to decay. The food becomes so unpleasant that people will not eat it. These are referred to as **food spoilage bacteria**. They have an important role in nature by decomposing dead vegetable and animal matter and thus aiding the essential recycling process. Fungi such as moulds can also cause food to spoil.

Spores

Some kinds of bacteria are able to form spores. These have a protective outer coat which keeps bacteria alive but inactive, in situations that normally would kill them. Later, if conditions become suitable, the spores change into the usual form of bacteria that then multiply rapidly.

Spores can withstand high cooking temperatures and are able to survive situations where nutrients or moisture are not immediately available.

How they grow

Bacteria are living things like ourselves and must have food, moisture, warmth, and time to live and grow.

Food

Certain foods - most of which have a high protein content - are particularly rich in nutrients and contain moisture. They therefore provide excellent conditions for bacterial growth if kept in warm conditions. When these foods are ready to eat without further treatment such as cooking which would kill bacteria, they are known as high risk foods.

High risk foods are blamed in at least 75% of all cases of food poisoning. The main categories of high risk foods are:

- **Cooked meat and poultry and cooked meat products, such as gravy, soup and stock**

These moist foods are particularly rich in the nutrients that bacteria need to grow. If kept under warm conditions even a small number of bacteria will become many millions in a short time.

- **Milk and eggs and products made from them**

Milk and eggs, and foods containing milk and eggs such as cream, custard and mayonnaise are often involved in cases of food poisoning. Usually this is because they have been kept in warm conditions or have been contaminated by a food handler.

Certain types of cheese are also high risk. Some types of soft cheeses are frequently associated with a particular bacteria called Listeria.

- **Shellfish**

Shellfish such as mussels, oysters, prawns, crabs and lobsters may pick up food poisoning bacteria and viruses from polluted water. The risk to humans is greatest if the shellfish are eaten raw, for example, oysters.

- **Cooked rice**

Bacterial spores can be found in dry rice: once water is added to the rice during cooking the bacteria become active. Some of the bacterial spores may survive the cooking temperature. If, following cooking, the rice is not eaten immediately or not refrigerated, these spores change back into bacteria and grow rapidly. They produce a toxin which is not destroyed by reheating.

Foods containing sugar, salt or acid - such as jam or pickles - discourage the growth of bacteria. Some foods have preservatives (chemical substances) added to them to restrict the growth of bacteria.

Bacterial growth may also be affected by the presence or absence of oxygen.

There is more information on how bacteria are affected by acid and oxygen in the Appendix.

Moisture

To grow, bacteria need moisture and this can be found in many foods including the high risk foods.

Bacteria are less likely to survive in dried food such as powdered milk or dried eggs but any bacteria that do survive under such dry conditions begin to grow again if fluids are added to the food.

One of the reasons why sugar and salt discourage the growth of bacteria is that they take up the moisture and prevent the bacteria from using it. Similarly, when food is frozen its moisture turns into ice and is not available to the bacteria.

Warmth

The temperatures referred to throughout the book are in degrees Celsius (°C)

Bacteria that cause food poisoning will grow at temperatures between 5°C and 63°C; they grow most quickly at a temperature of around 37°C, which is the normal temperature of the human body.

For this reason, the range of temperatures between 5°C and 63°C is known as the **Temperature Danger Zone.**

Even a small number of bacteria can grow rapidly in food that is allowed to remain in the Temperature Danger Zone, for example, in a warm kitchen.

Pasteurisation is a method of destroying bacteria by rapidly heating the food to a sufficiently high temperature. Milk, liquid egg, ice cream and certain canned foods are examples of food treated in this way.

Temperatures outside the Danger Zone are less suitable for bacteria. Although bacteria need warmth they are usually killed by heat. Most bacteria are killed by temperatures at or above 70°C. Some bacteria and their toxins (poisons) can survive higher temperatures.

In cold conditions, that is below 5°C, bacteria do not grow or grow only very slowly. At very low temperatures some will die, but many will survive and grow again if warm conditions return.

Store ready-to-eat high risk foods below 5°C or above 63°C

Time

Given moist, warm food, bacteria need time to grow. It is often carelessness that allows them the time they need, such as when food is allowed to remain in the Temperature Danger Zone.

Each bacterial cell multiplies by splitting itself into 2 so that 1 bacterial cell becomes 2 bacterial cells. Each of these 2 bacteria then split to make 4 bacteria. Each of the 4 bacteria split into 2 again, making 8 bacteria, and so on.

If the temperature is suitable, bacteria will reproduce in this way about every 20 minutes.

This means that, given good conditions, 1 bacterium will have multiplied into many thousands in 4-5 hours. In practice, the numbers will be even greater because contaminated food is usually contaminated by more than one bacterium at the start.

Food poisoning bacteria are invisible to the naked eye and do not usually cause any change to the appearance, smell or taste of food. You cannot, therefore, rely on your senses to tell if food is contaminated by these bacteria.

FOOD   **MOISTURE**

WARMTH   **TIME**

If these four conditions come together bacteria will multiply

THE LIFE AND DEATH OF BACTERIA
Temperatures and bacterial growth

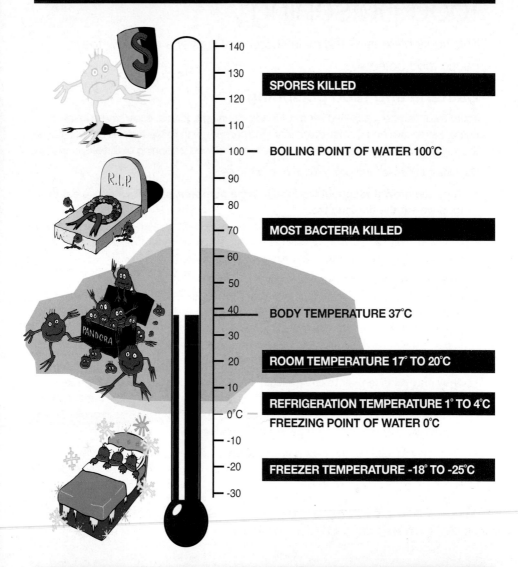

- 140
- 130

SPORES KILLED

- 120
- 110
- 100 — BOILING POINT OF WATER 100°C
- 90
- 80
- 70

MOST BACTERIA KILLED

- 60
- 50
- 40   BODY TEMPERATURE 37°C
- 30
- 20

ROOM TEMPERATURE 17° TO 20°C

- 10

REFRIGERATION TEMPERATURE 1° TO 4°C

- 0°C — FREEZING POINT OF WATER 0°C
- -10
- -20

FREEZER TEMPERATURE -18° TO -25°C

- -30

REMEMBER THE TEMPERATURE
DANGER ZONE 5° TO 63° C

How bacteria cause food poisoning

This section explains the main sources of bacteria and how they cause food poisoning.

Bacteria and food poisoning

There are a number of different kinds of food poisoning bacteria, each having its own name. *Salmonella* and *Campylobacter* are the names given to the families of bacteria that are responsible for a large proportion of the reported food poisoning outbreaks in the UK.

Bacteria can cause food poisoning in different ways:

- **They can grow throughout the food in large numbers, so that when we eat the food we eat the bacteria too.**
  For example, a number of *Salmonella* bacteria could be transferred to cold roast beef by slicing it with an unwashed knife previously used for cutting up a raw chicken. If the beef is left out in a warm kitchen, many millions of bacteria will grow.

- **They may be difficult to kill with heat.**
  An example of this is *Clostridium perfringens*, which is often found in raw meat and poultry. It is able to change into spores. Some of these spores can survive the cooking process. If a joint of meat, in which just a few spores have survived cooking, is left to cool slowly in a warm kitchen, a dangerously high number of bacteria will be found because the spores will change back into the usual form of bacteria and multiply.

- **They may release their toxins (poison) into the food before the food is eaten.**
  An example of this is called *Staphylococcus aureus* (found in our nose, throat and wounds) which can produce poisons in custards and trifles as well as in cooked meat and poultry, if allowed time to grow in warm conditions.

- **They may multiply in the gastrointestinal tract (gut).**
  An example of this is *Campylobacter*. This organism is now the biggest single identified cause of bacterial food poisoning.

Toxins are poisons produced by some bacteria as they grow in food or in the intestine.

A catering firm was shut down by Environmental Health Practitioners after police officers suffered food poisoning. Two hundred officers were in Birmingham to marshall a demonstration in July 2009, when 47 (24%) were struck down with severe diarrhoea and vomiting. Several were taken to hospital suffering from dehydration.

The sickness was suspected of being "food poisoning as a result of packed lunches issued to the officers". Locally prepared sandwiches were stored, unrefrigerated, in a van before being eaten on what was one of the hottest days of the summer. Symptoms of vomiting and diarrhoea were experienced 30-60 minutes after sandwiches were eaten and 10 of the cases were taken to hospital. A toxin was detected in one of the sandwiches and high numbers of bacteria were found in a number of sandwiches with different fillings. It was thought the bacteria came from an infected cut on the hand of a person involved in the sandwich preparation.

Sources of food poisoning bacteria

Before you can protect food from bacteria you need to know where the bacteria come from and how they come to be present in the food we eat. Most come from animal and human sources.

Raw foods

Many types of bacteria live in the intestines, or 'gut', of animals. The animals concerned usually have no symptoms, and just carry the bacteria. Thus bacteria can be transferred to meat intended for human consumption, particularly during slaughter.

For this reason, it is wise to think of all raw meat and poultry, as well as the juices that come from them, as already carrying many food poisoning bacteria before they arrive in the food area. Raw meat and raw poultry are frequent sources of food poisoning bacteria.

Other raw foods that may carry food poisoning bacteria are eggs — both inside and on the shell — and seafood such as oysters and mussels. Rice can also be contaminated. Many raw foods, including those used in salads, are naturally contaminated by bacteria from the soil.

In 2008, there was an international outbreak of food poisoning caused by *Salmonella*. This was traced to herbs grown in Israel.

It is important to wash herbs and salads, particularly if they are to be eaten without cooking.

When you handle and prepare raw foods, follow the rules for good hygiene control described in the next section and on pages 22-26.

Sources of food poisoning bacteria

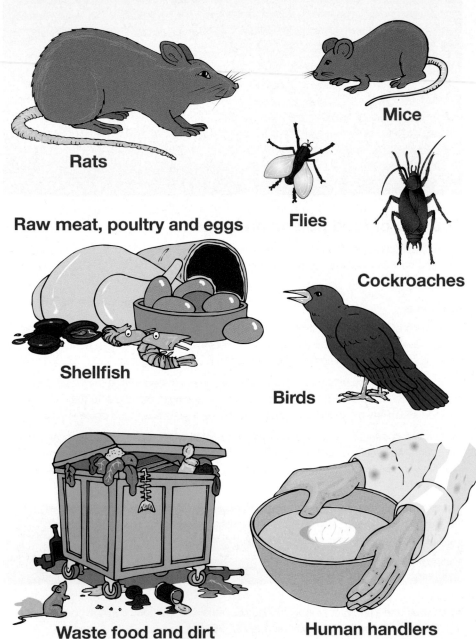

Rats

Mice

Flies

Cockroaches

Raw meat, poultry and eggs

Shellfish

Birds

Waste food and dirt

Human handlers

Ways in which *Staphylococcus aureus* enters food

Sneezing and coughing

Nose picking

Scratching your head

Handling food when you have a septic cut

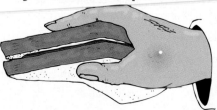

Smoking

The human body

Bacteria that can cause food poisoning are present in several areas of your own body, for example *Staphylococcus aureus* may be found on your hands and skin, in your nose, throat, mouth, ears, hair and fingernails. Bacteria that cause food poisoning, such as Salmonella, can also be present in our intestines, and thus in faeces (stools).

People infected with food poisoning bacteria often have no symptoms and are referred to as 'carriers' because, although not feeling ill themselves, they can transfer the infection to foods with their hands unless they are careful about their personal hygiene.

Careless food handling is one of the causes of bacterial contamination – with bacteria being transferred from hands, mouth and nose or from cuts, grazes, scratches and boils.

A way in which harmful bacteria *(Salmonella, Campylobacter, E. coli & Clostridium perfringens)* get into food

After using the toilet without washing your hands, bacteria can transfer from your gut to the food you handle

Other sources within the environment

Pests, including flies, insects, birds, rats and mice, carry bacteria on their bodies and in their urine and droppings. They can infect food or places where food may be placed.

Pets, too, carry bacteria on and in their bodies and should not be allowed into food areas.

Waste food and **rubbish** provide ideal conditions in which bacteria can live and reproduce because they are warm and are left undisturbed for several hours.

Hygiene control

This section gives details of action you should take to prevent food becoming contaminated.

Contamination

Hygiene control is the use of practices which will reduce the risk of food becoming contaminated. The aim of hygiene control is to prevent the spread of bacteria.

Food can be contaminated:

- through contact with contaminated foods, particularly raw meat and poultry
- through contact with work-surfaces and equipment
- by the food handler
- by pests
- by waste food and rubbish

The transfer of bacteria from a contaminated food to an uncontaminated food is called **cross-contamination.**

Food-to-food contamination

Always assume that raw meat and especially raw poultry are heavily infected with bacteria when brought into the food area. So keep raw meat and poultry including their juices, well away from other foods but particularly from cooked meat and cooked poultry.

Many other raw foods carry bacteria that will infect other foods if they come into contact. Take special care with **shellfish, eggs,** and **soil from vegetables.**

To prevent cross-contamination from raw foods you should:

- have different areas of the kitchen for preparing raw meat or poultry and foods that will be eaten without having any further treatment (e.g. cooking) that would destroy any bacteria that might get on to them

- use different refrigerators for storing raw and cooked foods but, if only one refrigerator is available, keep the raw foods on the lower shelves and the other foods above them.

Equipment-to-food contamination

Equipment and work-surfaces can easily become contaminated by foods particularly raw meat and poultry, by pests and even by the food handler. Then the contaminated surface or equipment will pass on the bacteria to food with which it comes into contact.

Treat as contaminated any items that have come into contact with raw meat and poultry or their juices, including work-surfaces, chopping boards, utensils, trays and equipment such as mincers, slicers and knives. These items often retain small pieces of raw food that can carry bacteria.

Equipment and work surfaces must be cleaned immediately after use. Otherwise, there is a risk of someone else using them without realising they might be contaminated.

Work-surfaces and equipment that look clean may have become contaminated by insects or even humans, but you cannot tell simply by looking. You will never see the bacteria but they may be there!

You must:

- thoroughly and immediately clean work-surfaces where raw meat and poultry have been handled
- keep utensils and equipment used in the preparation of raw meats and poultry separate from those used for other foods
- maintain a high standard of general cleanliness of worktops and equipment

Colour coding

Separation of utensils and equipment can be achieved through colour coding. Under colour coding, items of equipment such as knife handles, chopping boards and wiping cloths are given different colours to show when and where they should be used.

Example of colour coding system

Colour	Knives, chopping boards, cloths etc. to be used only for:
RED	RAW MEAT AND POULTRY
BLUE	FISH
YELLOW	COOKED MEATS
GREEN	SALAD AND FRUIT
ORANGE	VEGETABLES
WHITE	GENERAL PURPOSE/BAKERY

Wiping cloths pick up bacteria when used for cleaning. Once on a cloth, the bacteria can easily be transferred to other parts of the food area. There is a special danger if the cloth is used for wiping areas where raw meat and poultry have been lying and is then used somewhere else.

So, although we think of wiping cloths as a means of keeping things clean, they can just as easily become a means of spreading bacteria.

Always:

- keep separate wiping cloths for use with the different kinds of foods
- keep wiping cloths used in raw food areas out of other food areas
- use disposable wiping cloths, if available
- work with clean cloths - boil cloths frequently and keep in a solution of fresh sanitiser between uses.

Food handler-to-food contamination

To reduce the risk of you contaminating food:

- use tongs, food bags or food wrapping paper to pick up items of food
- carry food in containers, or on trays or plates
- avoid touching parts of dishes and cutlery that will come into contact with food, touch food as little as possible with your bare hands, use cutlery only once for tasting food - then wash it thoroughly before re-use
- do not lick your fingers to separate wrapping paper or blow into a food bag to open it

Maintaining a high standard of **personal hygiene** to prevent contamination of food is dealt with in the next section.

If disposable gloves are used it is essential that they are changed as often as you would need to wash your hands.

Other ways of contaminating food

Prepared food should be safely stored at the correct temperature and removed only a short time before it is served. But even in this short 'stand out' time there can be contamination by pests, particularly flies, and from bacteria in waste food or in the atmosphere generally. Food manufacturers should store finished products in a separate part of the building to other materials.

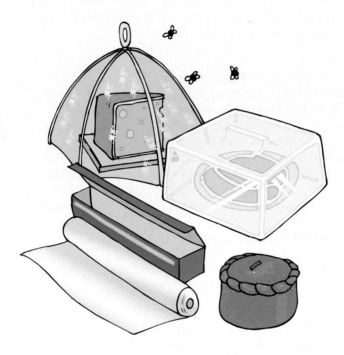

Personal hygiene

This section explains why high standards of personal hygiene are necessary and how these can be achieved.

Personal responsibilities

Bacteria live in and on your own body and can enter into food in the workplace if you do not maintain high standards of personal hygiene.

Hands

One of the easiest ways for bacteria to spread through the food area is from your hands. More than any other part of your body, your hands come into direct contact with food. Your hands also touch and can contaminate work surfaces, trays, crockery and catering utensils, which in turn may transfer the bacteria to food. Thus it is important to always wash your hands thoroughly using hot water and soap (preferably antibacterial liquid soap). Wash all parts of your hands and wrists under warm running water. The most frequently missed areas when washing hands are the fingertips and thumbs (the parts most likely to come into contact with food!). It is just as important to dry your hands thoroughly, preferably using disposable towels. Remember that if your hands are contaminated by bacteria then these can be passed on to taps so these require frequent cleaning.

Times when you must wash your hands include:

* before entering the food area and before touching any food
* after handling raw meat, poultry, shellfish, eggs or vegetables
* after using the lavatory
* after coughing into your hands or using a handkerchief
* after touching your face or hair
* after handling rubbish or cleaning

Bacteria can collect under fingernails. Nail varnish may flake off and contaminate food and false nails may become physical contaminants in food. It is important that you keep nails short and clean and do not wear nail varnish or false nails.

Always wash your hands before handling food

After using the toilet

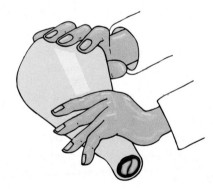

After handling raw foods

After cleaning

Personal responsibilities

Bacteria live in your nose, mouth, throat and ears and can be transferred by you to food, work surfaces and equipment. Bacteria also live in your hair and on your scalp. Unwashed hair carries more bacteria, and your hair can easily fall into food.

You should:

- avoid coughing or sneezing in a food room
- avoid touching your face and head, particularly your mouth, nose and ears
- keep your hair covered with a net or a hat
- wash your hair frequently
- never comb your hair in a food area or while wearing protective clothing.

Someone you know?

Jewellery

Jewellery and watches must not be worn in a food area. Bacteria and food can build up on items such as rings and bracelets.

Jewellery may fall into food. The advice is do not wear jewellery at work (an exception may be made for a plain ring).

Wounds

Wounds - cuts, grazes, scratches and boils - can quickly become infected with bacteria. The best way to prevent them from spreading to the food you handle is to make sure that all such wounds are properly covered.

You must:

- keep all wounds covered by coloured waterproof dressings
- tell your supervisor you are wearing a dressing: you may not be allowed to handle food

Protective clothing

Food handlers must wear suitable clean clothing. Protective clothing should be worn where appropriate, but remember it must be kept clean.

Your everyday clothes can bring bacteria into the food area. The purpose of protective over-clothing or kitchen uniform is to prevent contamination from this source. But you can also spread bacteria if the over-clothing or uniform is dirty.

It will help to protect the food from the risk of contamination if you:

- wear clean protective clothing where appropriate

- do not wear your protective clothing away from work

Smoking

Smoking is not allowed in any work area. Bacteria can be transferred to your hands from your mouth by smoking so hands must be washed when returning from a smoking break.

Reporting illness

Should you feel unwell or be suffering from a stomach disorder, cold or cough, or from an eye or ear discharge, report it to your supervisor. Also let them know if someone where you live seems to be suffering from a stomach bug.

Your employer may require other illnesses to be reported e.g. if you have been ill whilst you were on holiday, as you might have picked up a more infectious or unusual illness.

If you visit a doctor because of any of these complaints, tell the doctor you are a food handler.

Pest control

This section tells you about pests, the preventive action that you can take and the need to seek expert help.

Pests and food

Three kinds of pests are commonly found in places where food for human consumption is prepared or stored:

- **Rodents** - such as mice and rats
- **Insects** - such as houseflies, cockroaches and ants
- **Birds** - such as pigeons, magpies and sparrows

These pests eat and spoil food. They also transfer the food poisoning bacteria they carry on their bodies and in their droppings to the food.

Preventing access

Pests seek food, warmth and shelter. Take steps to keep them out. You should:

- keep doors and windows closed so far as is possible
- use fly screens on windows
- check deliveries for pests
- find the ways by which pests gain access
- do not do anything to attract pests to the premises, for example, by leaving kitchen waste uncovered in the outside bin.

Denying pests favourable conditions

You can never be sure that pests will be kept out. But you can limit the pests' opportunities for contaminating food and the workplace.

To do this, adopt the following good working practices:

- promptly remove food particles and spillages from work surfaces and floors
- do not leave dirty utensils and equipment lying around
- maintain a high standard of general cleaning
- do not leave food out overnight
- store dried foods in tightly lidded containers (this will also prevent moisture entering the food)
- regularly check all food storage areas for signs of pests
- empty internal waste bins regularly throughout the day and daily at close of work
- keep lids on external waste bins/skips/oil containers and do not store waste outside of these containers

Common pests

Rats and mice

Mice can enter premises through a hole no larger than the thickness of a pencil and young rats through one not much bigger.

Once established within premises these pests are difficult to remove because of their high rate of breeding and resistance to chemical poisons called rodenticides. They will make nests in or near food premises using old packaging and food refuse.

Rats and mice carry bacteria on their fur and feet, and in their droppings and urine. They contaminate and spoil food in addition to eating it. In particular, they will eat stored food and this is one reason why you must frequently check and clean storage areas.

Usually, removal of rodents requires specialist treatment but the food handler can play a major role in making sure that they are not attracted to the premises in the first place. High standards of cleanliness and food protection are essential.

Houseflies

Houseflies usually enter food premises through open doors, open windows and air vents.

The pests breed from May to September anywhere where there is rotting food, faecal matter or general refuse.

Just as they will breed anywhere, houseflies will feed anywhere and may have enjoyed a meal in a sewer minutes before settling on a cream cake in your servery.

A housefly will vomit on the food it is eating and its legs and body will further contaminate the food. Then it will depart – usually unseen. If you needed only one reason for covering food at all times the housefly would provide it!

Do not use insecticides in a food area unless under expert guidance. The ultra-violet electronic insect killer attracts then kills insects that then fall into a tray. The equipment must be sited well away from a light source and from any part of the food area where open food is dealt with, so dead insects don't fall into the food. Frequent and careful clearing of the tray is necessary. Make sure that the bulbs are changed regularly or they may no longer attract insects.

Cockroaches

These pests are difficult to spot. Cockroaches live behind woodwork and in drains and other difficult to reach places. They also like warm areas such as inside cabinets. They may be brought into premises with incoming food supplies so always check these carefully. Cockroaches come out at night.

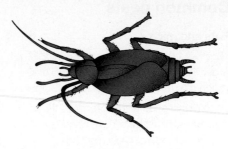

Removing an infestation of cockroaches is a specialist task requiring the use of specialist chemicals, but the food handler can play a preventive role by keeping all surfaces, floors and walls clean, and by generally avoiding a build-up of grease or food residues. Bins must be thoroughly cleaned otherwise the cockroaches will breed in them.

Birds

Birds gain access through doors and windows. Many commonly found birds scavenge for domestic food and contaminate food supplies through contact with their bodies, beaks or from their droppings.

Once established, birds are difficult to get rid of and this increases the importance of preventive measures. Outside bins must be lidded, with no refuse lying around. Birds thrive in the vicinity of take-away food shops and open-air eating places unless you make sure that uneaten food is binned promptly and the area is kept especially clean.

Professional pest controllers use nets and baits to trap birds and employ various methods to deny them perches.

Cats, kittens, dogs, puppies and cage birds carry food poisoning bacteria and in the wrong place – the food area for instance – pets can become pests.

Finding pests

Always look for the following signs:

- droppings
- greasy trails at the base of walls and around equipment
- marks on food or small mounds of food debris
- nibbled wrappings and holes in cardboard containers
- pest bodies
- unusual smells and noises
- damage to woodwork.

The food handler starting work early in the morning should be particularly vigilant in looking for the tell-tale signs - many pests are active at night.

Get rid of food that you suspect may have been contaminated by pests

Getting rid of pests

If you find signs of pests or suspect that the work-place is infested, you must immediately tell your supervisor. Expert advice can be obtained from specialist private contractors, but you should ensure that they are properly qualified. One way of ensuring this is to use members of the BPCA (British Pest Control Association).

The main steps that can be taken are:

- trapping and catching pests such as rodents and insects
- laying poisons or other chemical substances

Poisoned baits, powders, etc. may be used but only where authorised and under expert supervision. Special cleaning of floors and surfaces may be necessary after such operations.

Poisons and chemicals must be handled with great care, kept away from food and be stored in a secure place.

Kitchen design and layout

This section describes the standard of workplace that you should expect.

The hygienic kitchen

The design and layout of your kitchen can affect the standard of food hygiene that you can achieve.

A hygienic kitchen layout is one that allows plenty of space for work and storage, and provides separate working areas for each of the food categories – raw, high risk, vegetables and other. A key objective is to separate clean areas from dirty areas of operation.

Work surfaces

As work-surfaces are constantly in use, they must be strong, long-lasting, and easily cleaned. Stainless steel tables with hollow steel legs are ideal. Braked wheels on the base of work-surfaces and other items of equipment allow them to be moved out of the way when the floor or walls are being cleaned.

Floors

A kitchen floor must be hard wearing, easy to clean, non-absorbent, and non-slip. It should be resistant to acids, fat and grease.

The floor should be free of cracks and be coved at an angle with the wall. This will prevent food particles, dirt and grease – all of which can carry bacteria – from building up in areas where they are difficult to remove.

Walls

Walls should be smooth and free from cracks - smooth plaster provides a suitable surface - with glazed tiles being used in those areas where the walls are likely to be splashed, such as behind sinks and above work-surfaces. Walls should be painted a light colour to show up dirt and grease.

Ceilings

Ceilings should be smooth, light in colour, and coved at an angle where they meet the walls.

Ventilation

An effective system of ventilation is essential to remove the heat, steam, condensation and cooking odours of the kitchen and to provide proper working conditions for the staff. A stuffy, moist room helps bacteria to grow.

Lighting

Kitchens must be well lit by natural or artificial lighting. Poor lighting makes it difficult to prepare food hygienically and to clean properly - and makes accidents more likely.

Sinks

Sinks should be provided for the washing of food and for any hand-washing of dishes and utensils. Sinks should provide hot and cold water and preferably be made of stainless steel.

Waste disposal

Waste food can be disposed of efficiently and immediately using a waste disposal machine that breaks down the food before flushing it away through a waste pipe.

Waste food not disposed of in this way and general refuse should be placed in strong plastic bags and placed in bins reserved for this purpose. The bins must have lids and be foot operated. Bins should not be sited near food preparation areas.

Toilets and washing facilities

Toilets must not lead directly onto food rooms.

Toilets must be well ventilated and there must be facilities for washing and drying hands.

Hand washing is less likely to be overlooked if the hand-wash basins are situated near the exit. A **'Now wash your hands'** notice should be posted nearby.

There should be at least one hand-wash basin in the kitchen and in easy reach of those preparing food. It is a good idea to site a wash basin at the entrance to the kitchen as well as close to all high risk food preparation areas.

Hand-wash basins should have hot and cold (or appropriately mixed) running water and be supplied with materials for cleaning and drying hands.

Workflow

Organising the kitchen into separate areas for separate jobs lies at the heart of hygienic kitchen design. The exact layout will depend upon the size of the kitchen as well as on the type of meals it prepares, but work must flow smoothly:

Delivery   Storage   Preparation   Service

Storage rooms, refrigerators and freezers should be near delivery areas.

Vegetables and fruit should be prepared near their place of storage, away from other preparation areas to prevent the spread of soil.

Raw meat and poultry must not be dealt with near other foods.

Organising the kitchen in this way reduces the risk of raw food coming near cooked food, or of waste food or refuse contaminating food preparation areas. But remember the importance of keeping your work area clean at all times.

Wood

Wood is unsuitable for use in the kitchen. Wood wears quickly, can splinter, is absorbent and can develop cracks in which bacteria can lodge. It is therefore unsuitable for use as floors, work surfaces or as items of equipment such as chopping boards.

Example of the layout of a hygienic kitchen

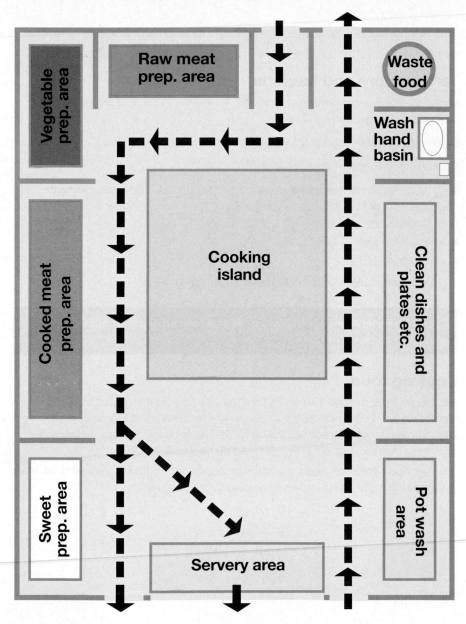

Separation of 'Clean' and 'Dirty' areas

Temperature control

This section specifies the action needed to avoid mistakes in the temperature control of food - the most common cause of problems.

Temperature and bacteria

Bacteria will grow rapidly in foods, particularly in high risk foods, that are left within the Temperature Danger Zone: 5°C - 63°C.

Bacteria do not grow or grow only very slowly, at temperatures below 5°C.

They do not grow at temperatures above 63°C.

The idea behind correct temperature control is to keep food – especially the high risk foods – out of the Temperature Danger Zone. The rules for achieving this are quite simple:

- keep hot food hot
- keep cold food cold
- keep prepared food out of the Temperature Danger Zone

Correct temperature control is the most powerful weapon against the growth of bacteria in food.

Cooking food

Bacteria are killed by heat. This is why food must be cooked thoroughly. Most bacteria will not survive in food that is cooked at a temperature of at least 70°C (the legal minimum temperature in Scotland is 82°C). This temperature must be reached *throughout the food, including the centre and be held for 2 minutes.*

However, some bacterial spores and some bacterial poisons (toxins) are destroyed only if subjected to higher temperatures for a greater length of time.

Meat and poultry

All meat and poultry must be thoroughly cooked because of the likelihood of bacterial contamination.

The larger the joint of meat or poultry carcass, the longer it will take for the heat to reach the centre. If the cooking is not at a high enough temperature and for long enough, the centre may not be heated sufficiently to kill the bacteria. However, just enough warmth may reach the centre of the food to keep it within the Temperature Danger Zone so enabling food poisoning bacteria to grow rapidly. The need for sufficiently high temperatures reaching the centre of the food must be kept in mind at all times. It is particularly important when cooking:

- **large joints of meat**

  Large, thick joints should be cut into smaller pieces for cooking so that heat sufficient to destroy bacteria will reach the centre of each piece much more quickly.

- **rolled meat joints, beef burgers and sausages**

  Bacteria are usually on the surface and are easily killed by cooking. However, in a rolled joint, beef burgers or sausages, bacteria that were on the surface become mixed throughout the food and it becomes more difficult for the heat to reach them.

- **poultry – particularly large carcasses**

  Poultry can carry large numbers of bacteria and these are spread through the whole carcass. Cooking must ensure that the carcass is sufficiently heated to kill the bacteria wherever they may be. When a carcass is large, it is bad practice to cook the bird with the stuffing inside. The highest load of bacteria is inside where the intestines were. The stuffing can prevent heat sufficient to kill the bacteria reaching the centre of the bird. It is better to cook the bird and the stuffing separately.

Soups and stocks

It is bad practice to add a freshly made batch of soup or stock to a quantity made earlier but only partly used. 'Topping up' is dangerous particularly when it continues over several services. During this time there will almost certainly be times when the temperature of the 'ever-on-the-go' pot will drop below the **63°C** required for safety. Then the bacteria will multiply rapidly in the rich, warm, liquid food. It is much safer if you:

- Prepare soups and stock in small amounts and throw away anything left over at the end of the day.

Eggs

Salmonella may still be found in a small percentage of UK eggs. As a safeguard eggs should be thoroughly cooked as imported eggs have been found to be contaminated.

- Do not use damaged or dirty eggs
- Use pooled eggs on the same day and do not top up
- Use pasteurised eggs for raw and lightly cooked foods e.g. home-made mayonnaise, béarnaise and hollandaise sauces, some salad dressings, ice cream, icing, mousse, tiramisu
- Buy eggs from a reputable supplier
- Store eggs in a cool, dry place, ideally in the fridge

Keeping hot foods hot

High risk foods eaten immediately following cooking are safe providing the cooking temperature has been high enough.

If the food is not served immediately, it is necessary to use equipment that will hold the food at a temperature of 63°C or above. Heated trolleys and cupboards and heated food service counters are examples of such equipment.

Key points in their use are:

- heat the equipment to operating temperature before food is loaded
- ensure that the food is already fully cooked and at a temperature of at least 63°C at the time of loading
- never use the equipment to heat up cold or partially heated food

Keeping cold foods cold

Many foods that are eaten cold have sufficient nutrients and moisture to enable bacteria to grow quickly. Cold meats and poultry, prepared salads, pâtés, soft cheeses, sweets and cream are examples.

The rules for foods that will be eaten cold are:

- keep refrigerated until as near as possible to the time of serving
- handle as little as possible
- keep away from other foods
  - particularly raw foods
  - keep covered

Keeping prepared food out of the Temperature Danger Zone

If food is not to be served within a very short time of its being cooked, it should be cooled to under 8°C as quickly as possible after cooking. It must be refrigerated as soon as cooling is complete.

Quick cooling is important. The food will pass through the Temperature Danger Zone while it is cooling. It must spend as short a period as possible in the 'Zone' because bacteria may have survived the cooking process and will multiply if given time.

Rapid cooling will be helped by:

- dividing food into smaller portions
- transferring the cooked foods to a cold container that is then put in ice-cold water
- placing the food in the coolest part of the workplace (providing this does not carry the risk of cross-contamination)
- using a blast chiller

Re-heating cooked foods

Re-heated cooked foods - notably poultry and meat - are the cause of many cases of food poisoning. Food handlers often make the mistake of thinking that because food has already been cooked it is free of bacteria and that a 'warming up' will be sufficient. For example, roast meat should not be reheated by adding hot gravy.

Some bacteria - particularly in spore form - may not have been killed by the cooking. Following cooking, the food may have become contaminated by a food handler's hands or through cross-contamination.

If contaminated food is only lightly warmed instead of being thoroughly re-heated, bacteria will have ideal conditions for growth.

Follow these guidelines for food that is to be re-heated:

- do not remove the food from the refrigerator too far in advance of re-heating
- handle the food as little as possible and keep it covered and away from other foods
- divide large items into smaller portions
- heat the food to at least 70°C (82°C in Scotland) at its core for at least 2 minutes
- serve quickly following re-heating
- NEVER re-heat cooked food more than once

NOTE: If re-heating a ready-made cooked meal such as may be purchased in a supermarket, follow the manufacturer's instructions in addition to the advice given above

Refrigeration

A refrigerator should operate at between 1°C and 4°C.

Placing food in a refrigerator does not kill the bacteria that the food may be carrying, but the low temperature means that warmth - one of the requirements for bacterial growth - is not present. The bacteria simply stop growing. If the food is removed from the refrigerator into room temperature the bacteria will begin to grow again.

Foods should be refrigerated for only short periods of time, the duration varying from food to food. Most foods fall within the 1-5 days range but a few can be refrigerated for longer. Package labels often state the maximum periods of refrigeration. Food in a refrigerator should be checked regularly to make sure it is removed and eaten by its 'use by' date. Any food prepared and refrigerated should be given a 'use by' date.

You should always refrigerate high risk foods and raw meat, poultry, eggs and seafood.

Points to remember about refrigeration:

- keep raw meat and poultry away from other foods - especially cooked meat and cooked poultry
- make sure that nothing - particularly blood from raw meat and poultry - can drip on to food below
- NEVER place cooked food in the refrigerator immediately after cooking: allow it to cool first
- keep all food covered. If food is wrapped use food grade materials
- do not crowd food into the refrigerator – leave enough room for cold air to circulate. When packing refrigerated display units or freezers, ensure that you do not fill above the relevant 'load line' or obstruct air inlets
- check the temperature of the refrigerator is between 1°C and 4°C at least twice a day (See Record Chart overleaf)
- open refrigerator doors as little as possible and close them quickly
- defrost the refrigerator regularly to prevent the build-up of ice, and keep it clean
- date label all food placed in the refrigerator.

Temperature Record Sheet – suggested headings

TEMPERATURE RECORD SHEET
Raw Meat Refrigerator No. _____
Temperature range 1°C – 4°C

Date	Time	°C	Comments	Signature

To keep within the law you must keep chilled food at or below 8°C.

There are some harmful bacteria that can still grow at lower temperatures. The risk is small but you are advised to store all food requiring refrigeration at 1°C - 4°C.

Freezing
Freezers keep food at a temperature (-18°C to -25°C) well below freezing point. Freezing denies bacteria the warmth they need to grow. The coldness also turns any moisture in the food into ice - water in a form that bacteria cannot use.
Some bacteria will die as a result of freezing but others will survive, although they will be unable to grow. However, these surviving bacteria will grow if the temperature rises towards the Temperature Danger Zone.

The length of time food can be stored in a frozen state depends on the type of food and the rating of the freezing unit. Although frozen food may not become contaminated it may deteriorate in flavour and character if stored too long. Different foods have different storage times ranging from 2 to 12 months. Check with the supplier of the food if you do not know how long it can remain frozen. If you are a caterer freezing food on the premises you should store it for a maximum of 1 month.

Points to remember about freezing:

- the freezer should lower the temperature of the food to -22°C. The temperature of the freezer must not rise above -18°C. Check daily
- wrap, label and date all food using food grade materials
- store food neatly within the freezer and do not overload
- use old stock before new - know the maximum storage periods.

Thawing food

Small items of food such as thin chops, fish cutlets, vegetables and many convenience foods can be cooked from frozen without being thawed first.

But you cannot do this with poultry, joints of meat and bulky items of food. In general, these foods MUST be completely thawed before cooking begins. Unless complete thawing occurs, the temperature at the core of the food may not reach a high enough level during the cooking process to kill bacteria.

Food has been completely thawed once it is soft and there are no ice crystals present. The legs of properly thawed poultry can be moved quite easily.

Thawing can cause problems because when the outer surface of food warms up bacteria can begin to grow although the centre of the food remains frozen.

Thawing methods – raw meat and poultry

Many microwave ovens have a defrosting facility which must be used strictly according to manufacturer's instructions. Special thawing cabinets are also available. The time required to thaw meat or poultry depends upon the size of the piece and the temperature at which thawing is taking place.

GUIDANCE ON THAWING TIMES		
	REFRIGERATOR	COOL ROOM
POULTRY		
1.5 kg (3.3lb)	24 hrs	10hrs
4 kg (8.8lb)	60hrs	20hrs
MEAT JOINTS		
1 kg (2.2lbs)	8hrs	4hrs
3 kg (6.6lbs)	42hrs	16hrs

When thawing raw meat and poultry:

- plan well ahead: know where you will be thawing and allow sufficient time for the process
- place the frozen meat or poultry in a container to catch any liquid that drains off
- cover the thawing food
- keep the thawing food away from other foods, utensils and work-surfaces
- following thawing, cook the food immediately
- once frozen food has been thawed, never re-freeze it!

Measurement of temperature

The food handler should be able to measure temperatures, for example, those reached at the centre of foods during cooking or within a refrigerator.

Probe thermometers can be inserted into foods with the temperature indicated by a dial or digital display. However, probes can pick up bacteria and should be cleaned both before and after use using a disinfectant wipe or by thorough washing and sanitising.

To measure the temperature within a refrigerator use a thermometer designed for this purpose. Place it on the top shelf. Normally, this is the warmest part of the interior. You should also measure the temperature of food within the fridge using a probe thermometer. You can use a specifically designed test gel or a container of water kept in the fridge for this purpose.

Make a practice of taking frequent temperature checks on refrigerators and freezers and keep a record of them.

Temperature probes MUST be regularly checked for accuracy

Cook-chill and cook-freeze

Cook-chill is a system of food preparation that involves just what the name suggests. Immediately following thorough cooking, the food is rapidly chilled and then stored at a low temperature. Refrigerators and freezers are NOT suitable for chilling. Only purpose-built chilling equipment, for example, a blast-chiller, should be used. Once chilled, the food is transferred to a refrigerated store reserved for cook-chill food and capable of maintaining the food at between 1°C and 3°C.

A cook-chill product carries a 'Use by' date-mark based on its maximum safe life and this must be strictly observed. In general, cook-chill foods can be refrigerated for a maximum of 5 days including the day of production and the day it is eaten.

Cook-freeze has many similarities to cook-chill but in this system, following cooking, the food is rapidly frozen and then stored in freezers where it can remain for between 2 and 12 months depending on the particular food. The rules for re-heating and serving applicable to cook-chill foods apply equally to cook-freeze items.

Producing food by cook-chill and cook-freeze methods requires special equipment and rigorous working practices to ensure strict control of temperature and very high standards of hygiene.

Microwave ovens

Microwave ovens use electromagnetic energy (microwaves) to heat and defrost food.

There are domestic (home) and commercial (catering) models of microwave ovens. Commercial models are more powerful electrically and are constructed to stand up to more intensive use. Domestic models are unsuitable for commercial use.

All of the rules governing food preparation by conventional ovens apply also to microwave ovens. Food that is being cooked or re-heated must reach at least 70°C at the core and remain at this temperature long enough to destroy any bacteria (higher temperatures apply in Scotland).

Microwave cooking tends to heat food unevenly, 'cold' spots may result in bacteria not being destroyed.

To avoid food having 'hot' and 'cold' spots some ovens are fitted with a turntable so that all of the food can cook evenly. Always check that the food is hot throughout; if necessary, move the food around the oven or, if a liquid, stir to ensure adequate heating.

Dry food storage

All dry foods, such as flour, rice and pulses and all canned food, should be stored in a room or cupboard that is cool, dry, clean and ventilated.

Deliveries must be checked to ensure that goods that will be stored are free from odours, dampness or other forms of soiling and do not harbour pests.

Food should be stored on shelves – no food should be put on the floor – to reduce the risk of contamination by pests and to make the floor easier to clean.

'First in - first out' is one of the 'golden rules' of stock control. Stock should be rotated so that the oldest food is used first. Identifying the order of use will be easier if stocks are date-labelled and are not crowded together on the shelves.

It is important to keep food covered at all times. Food that is not pre-packed, such as rice, should be stored in containers with tight fitting lids.

Any cans that show signs of damage should be thrown away.

Cleaning and disinfection

This section describes some of the methods available for cleaning and disinfecting utensils and the workplace.

Cleaning the workplace

Cleaning should achieve two things:

- the removal of grease, food debris and dirt generally
- the destruction of bacteria (disinfection)

Cleaning of the workplace can be divided into two broad categories:

- clean-as-you-go
- scheduled cleaning

Clean-as-you-go applies to cleaning that must be done very quickly after use. The aim is to prevent cross-contamination or to keep working areas clean and tidy.

Examples of this type of cleaning are:

- washing and sanitising a chopping board after use
- cleaning up a floor spillage just after it has happened

Scheduled cleaning refers to cleaning tasks carried out at regular intervals. Food businesses should have a timetable or rota which lists all the details for each item to be cleaned. Examples of scheduled cleaning duties are:

- cleaning the kitchen floor (daily)
- cleaning shelves in the dry store (weekly)

Effective cleaning will be achieved if you consider:

- what is to be cleaned? Is it 'clean-as-you-go' or 'scheduled'? How often must it be cleaned, and at what times?
- who is responsible for the cleaning?
- what is the most appropriate type of method to be used?
- what cleaning equipment and chemicals are to be used?
- where are these materials to be stored?
- how can the cleaning be done safely?

Cleaning and disinfection chemicals

Chemicals are available to enable you to maintain proper standards of cleaning and disinfection. Usually the chemical is added to water to make the cleaning solution.

Detergents are chemicals that will dissolve grease and assist the removal of food debris and dirt. Detergents do not kill bacteria.

Disinfectants are chemicals designed to destroy bacteria. They reduce the number of bacteria to a safe level. Disinfectants are not effective in removing dirt and grease. Disinfectants which have a very strong smell that might affect the food must not be used on any surfaces or equipment that come into direct contact with food. It is very important that these surfaces are properly disinfected using a suitable chemical solution or steam or hot water (over 82°C).

Sanitizers are chemicals combining the role of both detergent and disinfectant. They are designed to remove grease and dirt and to disinfect in one operation.

Disinfection by **heat** is an effective way of killing bacteria, for example, using very hot water (over 82°C). Chemical disinfectants and sanitizers can be used in addition or in situations where hot water is not available. However they are less effective in water that is not hot and on surfaces that have not received a preliminary clean using hot water and a detergent.

When using cleaning solutions:

- follow the 'Instructions For Use' including those for dilution and storage
- wear rubber gloves or other protective clothing when necessary
- do not store chemicals within the food area or where warmth could increase their temperature
- make up fresh hot solutions frequently: dirty or cool water makes the chemicals less effective
- never mix different chemicals - they become less effective when mixed and you may produce poisonous gases.

Dish washing

Crockery, cutlery and utensils should be cleaned immediately after use. Cleaning can be by hand or by machine.

Washing by hand

The most hygienic way to wash by hand is with TWO stainless-steel sinks side by side. Wash in one and rinse in the other.

If you do not have two sinks, you can clean and then rinse in the same sink or wash in the sink and rinse in a separate bowl of hot water.

Rinse water should be changed frequently, when dirty or cooled. Rinsing is important. Laboratory tests have shown that dishes that are not rinsed are covered with large numbers of bacteria.

Washing by machine

There are several types of dish and utensil washing machines available but they all follow the stages of cleaning.

Correct loading of these machines is essential. Items should be stacked neatly so that the cleaning solution can reach them. Cups, glasses and jugs should be stacked upside-down to avoid collecting water.

Dishwashers must be properly maintained, and the recommended salts, powders and rinse aids used in the correct amounts.

Cleaning work-surfaces

It is vital that surfaces upon which food is prepared are kept clean and bacteria-free for each new job. Clean-as-you-go applies but there may also be a scheduled requirement to clean the surfaces at the daily start of work. Work-surfaces should be left clean and clear at close of work.

Cleaning other surfaces

Telephones, wash basin taps and handles on doors and refrigerators, are examples of surfaces where contaminated hands may deposit bacteria which can be picked up by other hands. Include such surfaces in the cleaning schedule.

Cleaning floors, walls and ceilings

Floors

Clean **all** areas of the floor paying particular attention to parts where food may have lodged.

Where cleaning is required during the day this can usually be done by mopping. Food spillages should be cleaned up as they occur.

A wet floor is a hazard to staff: therefore the floor should be dried after wet mopping rather than left to dry.

It is important that a floor is left clean and free from food residues at the daily close of work. Dirty floors are an invitation to pests.

Walls and ceilings

Most walls and ceilings can be satisfactorily cleaned using hot water and a detergent or sanitizer. A disinfectant should be used daily for wall areas where splashes and stains may occur such as behind sinks or work-surfaces.

Dusting and sweeping

Dry dusting and sweeping can fill the air with dust particles that may well be carrying bacteria. Use a moist cloth - never a dry duster - for ledges and shelves.

Scrubbers, mops and cloths

Scrubbers, mops and cloths become contaminated with bacteria during cleaning. They must be thoroughly washed and disinfected frequently. Mop heads and floor cloths should be changed regularly.

Waste bins

Within the food area

Bins and bin stands must be washed down and disinfected regularly, the task being included in the cleaning schedule. The floor area around bins must be cleaned at least daily.

Outside the food area

Outside waste bins and skips must be positioned as far away from the food area as is practicable and must have lids or covers to limit access by pests.

Keep the area around the bins tidy: do not leave waste material stacked up outside the bin or skip. Hose down the area after each collection. During the summer months it may be necessary to disinfect the bins or to spray them with insecticides.

CLEAN THOROUGHLY
Cleaning done badly simply spreads the bacteria!

HACCP systems

A HACCP based system is a food safety management system, which if used correctly, can help to ensure safe food production.

Food safety legislation requires a food business to have in place a documented system based on HACCP principles. The food business operator (the proprietor) is the person responsible for the development and management of a documented food safety system. Other staff such as managers or chefs can be asked to put controls into practice and carry out routine checks.

What is HACCP?

Hazard Analysis and Critical Control Points is a widely accepted food safety management system, which can be adapted to suit all sizes and types of food businesses. The main aim of HACCP is to focus attention on critical control points in the food business operation and to take measures to ensure that problems do not occur which could make the food unsafe.

It is essential that any business is committed to operating the system in full, otherwise the benefits will be reduced, the safety of the food put at risk and the business will not be obeying the law.

There are 7 basic principles to HACCP

1. Examine the process steps in the business and identify any hazards at these steps that must be prevented, eliminated or reduced to acceptable levels

2. Identify the Critical Control Points (CCP) at the steps where control is essential to prevent or eliminate a hazard or reduce it to acceptable levels

3. Establish critical limits at CCPs that show what must be done for the prevention, elimination or reduction of identified hazards

4. Establish and put in place effective monitoring procedures at CCPs

5. Establish corrective actions to take when monitoring shows that a CCP is not under control – i.e. the critical limit has not been met.

6. Establish procedures that you carry out regularly to verify that controls and monitoring are in place

7. Establish documents and records in line with the type and size of your business to show you have a formal food safety management system.

What are process steps?

Any catering operation may be thought of as a series of steps that take place in a certain sequence.

Generally the first step is the purchase of raw ingredients and the last step is the service or selling of the food a business produces.

A simple diagram of the common process steps in a catering business could be as follows;

PURCHASE

STORAGE

PREPARATION

COOKING

SERVICE

What are the hazards?

A hazard is anything which may cause harm to people who eat the food.

A HACCP based approach to food safety requires the identification of all of the hazards at each process step in a catering business; this is called 'hazard analysis'. It is at this point that you will need to think about what could go wrong in the business and then come up with measures that will control these hazards.

There are three types of hazard.

1. Microbiological hazards

This includes food poisoning bacteria such as *Salmonella, E. Coli* and *Bacillus cereus* which are hazardous because they can:

- survive cooking if already present in food and the food is cooked for too short a time or at too low a temperature, for example *Salmonella* in chicken;

- multiply to harmful levels in food given the right conditions, for example poor temperature control during storage, handling or hot holding;

- spread from raw foods such as meat, poultry and unwashed vegetables to cooked/ ready to eat foods either directly or via food handlers, work surfaces and equipment – this is known as cross-contamination.

Other microbiological hazards such as certain bacteria, yeasts and mould may lead to food spoilage.

2. Chemical hazards

These may already be present on certain foods as pesticides or insecticides. Chemical hazards may also arise from incorrect storage and the misuse of chemicals used in the food premises such as cleaning chemicals and rodent baits.

3. Physical hazards

These include contamination by materials such as glass, plastic, wood, metal, hair and pest bodies.

What are the control measures?

When the process steps and the hazards likely to occur have been identified, ways to prevent or control the hazards must be found. These are known as control measures.

Control measures may take many forms, for example:

Hazard	Control measure
The survival of harmful bacteria which may cause food poisoning	Cooking to core temperature of 70°C for 2 minutes
Spread (cross-contamination) of harmful bacteria from raw meat to cooked foods which may cause food poisoning	Using colour coded equipment e.g. cutting boards and knives

Critical control points (CCPs)

Critical control points are the stages of the process where the hazards must be controlled for the food to be safe to eat. All hazards at critical control points must be reduced to a safe level or eliminated by a suitable control measure.

CCP example no. 1 – cooling rice

If rice is cooled too slowly, it could give a customer food poisoning. The process step of 'cooling' is a critical control point (CCP).

CCP example no. 2 – cooking a burger or chicken from raw

If the burger or chicken is undercooked, any harmful bacteria present in the food will not be destroyed and the surviving bacteria could give a customer food poisoning. Cooking is the critical control point.

Critical limits

Critical limits are the safety limits set, for example a temperature range, at a critical control point to control the process at that CCP. The critical limit must be met to eliminate the hazard or reduce it to a safe level.

Monitoring

Part of the food safety system is the need to monitor the control measures at the critical control points. Monitoring will make sure critical limits are met.

A monitoring procedure might be taking the temperature of food in a fridge to see if it meets the critical limit temperature that has been set.

Records

The monitoring procedures chosen must be recorded. The way that this is done will depend on the size and nature of the business. Records need to be kept at the premises and regularly reviewed. One way of recording is by using a diary sheet. This is the method used in Safer Food Better Business (see HACCP systems below).

It is good practice for a supervisor to check monitoring records on a weekly basis. These records may need to be used to show that the business has taken the right steps to prepare food safely.

Corrective action

If, when monitoring takes place, the critical limit is not met, for example a refrigerator that should work at 4°C is actually found to be working at 14°C, action must be taken to put the situation right and make food safe or stop it being used. This is known as a 'corrective action'.

Corrective actions have two roles:

> Making food safe or stopping its use

AND

> Stopping the problem happening again – by looking at why there was a failure of the control measure and taking action to stop the problem happening again.

Verification

This is looking at the whole of the HACCP based system to ensure it is working properly. It also includes making sure that all procedures are being applied in day to day practice and that they are effective in controlling hazards.

An example of verification is checking that monitoring records are kept as a regular event and that they are accurate, or that corrective actions have been taken where something has gone wrong.

HACCP systems

The type of food safety management system in a food business will depend on its type and size. Practical guidance for retailers and food manufacturers are given in a range of industry guides. Small catering businesses requiring simple food hygiene management systems may benefit from packages, such as Safer Food, Better Business, CookSafe or Safe Catering. These have been specially designed for small catering businesses and are available free of charge from your Environmental Health Office or from the Food Standards Agency. These usually provide a simple explanation aimed at the owner or manager of how to identify hazards and CCPs in this type of business and simple forms in diary format which indicate the kind of checks, reporting procedures and records which need to be kept. Another suitable methodology for catering HACCP is 'assured safe catering'.

Before HACCP can be properly applied it is essential that a business follows GCP (Good Catering Practice) or GMP (Good Manufacturing Practice). These are the essential pre-requisites for HACCP and are detailed in industry guides. They cover areas such as structural standards, design, training and cleaning.

Hazard analysis: examples of critical control points
for a small business serving cold food only

Stage		Possible Hazard	Action Needed
Food is purchased		High risk foods which are to be eaten without further cooking are bought. Possible contamination with bacteria and/or toxins	Buy only high quality ingredients from reputable suppliers. Specify maximum temperature for transit and delivery
Food is received on premises		High risk food may already be contaminated	Check temperatures Check packaging Check date-mark
Storage of food		Growth of food poisoning organisms and/or possible further contamination	Wrap, label and store high risk food at correct temperature. Rotate stock and use by recommended date
Preparation of food		Contamination of high risk food by incorrect and extensive handling. Growth of bacteria	Wash hands before handling food. Use clean equipment. Limit time food is within the **Temperature Danger Zone.** Separate from any raw food
Cold holding of food		Growth of bacteria. Possible contamination	Ensure correct temperature. Limit time food is within the Temperature Danger Zone
Serving of prepared food		Growth of bacteria. Possible contamination	Serve directly from cold storage (refrigerator) or from cold holding (cold counter or display unit)

Food hygiene and the law

Everyone working with and handling food needs to understand the law as it relates to their business and themselves. More information is available from your local Environmental Health Practitioner. In addition, the Food Standards Agency website www.food.gov.uk, offers a range of free information guides on how the law affects food business owners. The following section picks out some points directly affecting the owners of food businesses from the large amount of law concerning food hygiene.

The Food Safety Act 1990

The Act is a major piece of legislation designed to protect the public against bad food or food that is misleadingly described. It enables Ministers to make Regulations and Orders. These can be made quickly, and are usually detailed and legally binding.

The European Union

Most of the legislation in the UK that concerns food safety is now set out by the European Union. Member states may be required to produce their own legislation to enforce certain EC Directives but EC Regulations have to be applied in all member states without modification. From 1st January 2006, a number of new food hygiene regulations applied in the UK. The regulations that are most important for food businesses are Regulation (EC) No. 852/2004 on the hygiene of foodstuffs and the Food Hygiene (England) Regulations 2006 (and equivalent regulations in Scotland, Wales and Northern Ireland). Regulation (EC) No.853/2004 is relevant to manufacturers of products of animal origin.

The Food Hygiene Regulations 2006

As far as the UK is concerned, the new regulations introduced on 1st January 2006 set out very clearly the duty of food businesses to produce food safely and to do this consistently.

- One set of hygiene and safety regulations covers all areas of the food chain from 'farm to fork'
- The owner of the food business is made responsible for ensuring that food handlers receive adequate instruction and/or training in food hygiene to enable them to handle food safely
- Food businesses, including catering businesses, are required to have a food safety management system based on the principles of HACCP
- The owner of the food business is responsible for ensuring that whoever is responsible for the HACCP-based procedures in the business has enough relevant knowledge and understanding to ensure the procedures are operated effectively.

Prevention of contamination of food by food handlers

Food handlers must:

- avoid exposing food to the risk of contamination

- report to their manager or supervisor if suffering from upset stomachs, infected wounds, colds and coughs

- keep themselves and their clothing clean and, where appropriate, wear clean protective clothing when on duty.

Food premises

There is a general requirement that a food business must not be carried out in unsanitary premises. Food premises must:

- be registered with the competent authority (usually the local authority) 28 days before the business can open or before starting to use new premises

- be maintained in good condition, kept clean and free from accumulation of waste and refuse

- have closed containers for the storage of waste, which must be protected against pests; proper arrangement should be made for the removal of waste

- have easy to clean, (and where necessary, disinfect), walls, floors and food contact areas

- be adequately supplied with clean water and proper drainage, be well lit and well ventilated

- be provided with hot/cold water sinks or other means for washing equipment, utensils and food and where necessary these must be separate from hand washing facilities

- be supplied with sufficient toilets, washbasins, soap and hygienic drying materials for the use of staff and where necessary adequate changing facilities must be provided

- have lavatories with sufficient ventilation, which do not lead directly into food rooms

- be designed and maintained to prevent access by pests

Equipment and transport

- food equipment must be kept clean

- it must be in good repair and condition so that it can be easily cleaned (and if necessary disinfected)

- vehicles or conveyances such as trolleys and/or containers used for transporting food must be kept clean and be in good repair and condition

- food wrapping materials must be properly stored and protected from contamination

- cleaning chemicals and disinfectants must not be stored in food handling areas

Food safety management systems

- food business operators must operate a food safety management system based on HACCP principles
- those responsible for the HACCP system must have enough relevant knowledge and understanding to ensure the system operates effectively
- the owner of the food business is responsible for ensuring that all food handlers receive adequate instruction and/or training in food hygiene to enable them to handle food safely.

Temperature control of food

Chilled holding requirements

- apply to foods known to be particularly vulnerable to contamination by food poisoning bacteria and such high risk food must be kept at or below 8°C
- high risk foods may remain on display or for service at above 8°C for four hours on a one-time only basis, or kept chilled at 8°C or below until used. If any food is left after this time it should be thrown away
- limited periods outside temperature control (loading, unloading, breakdowns) are permitted if there is no risk to food safety

Hot-holding requirements

- hot food on display must be kept at or above 63°C. It may be kept below 63°C for up to two hours for service and display on a one time only basis. Any food left after this time should be thrown away, reheated to 63°C or above or cooled as quickly as possible to 8°C or below. The food should be kept at a safe temperature until it is used.

Date marking of food

This is generally covered by the Food Labelling Regulations 1996. Highly perishable foods (including most pre-packaged food) must carry a 'Use by' date mark. It is an offence to sell food after this date. The food can be used up to and including the date shown.

Most other foods carry a 'Best before' date mark, indicating the date until which the food will be in the best condition for eating. Although it is not against the law to sell food after the 'Best before' date, it is, however an offence to sell unfit food.

Some foods are not required by law to bear a date mark - fresh fruit, vegetables, butchers meat, are examples, unless they are sold pre-packaged.

It is an offence for a date mark to be changed other than by the person responsible for the original date marking, or under the written authority of such a person.

Enforcing the law

Food authorities will deal with food hygiene offences under the Food Hygiene Regulations and food standards matters (food fraud etc) under the Food Safety Act 1990.

Local authorities must enforce the Food Hygiene Regulations on food businesses. The enforcement officer has the power to enter the food business premises at any reasonable hour and if necessary take away samples for analysis.

If an authorised officer has reasonable grounds for believing that a food business operator is failing to comply with the Hygiene Regulations, he may serve a Hygiene Improvement Notice or a Hygiene Emergency Prohibition Notice. Failure to comply with these is an offence.

Hygiene rules

What should I do?	Why should I do it?
Wash your hands • before entering the food area • after using the lavatory • between handling raw meat/poultry/ shellfish/eggs AND high-risk foods • before and after touching food • after coughing into your hands or using a handkerchief • after touching your face or hair • after carrying out any cleaning or handling rubbish	There are many bacteria on the surface of your skin. Most are harmless, but some can cause illness when transferred to food. In addition, your hands can pick up bacteria from other sources and contaminate food. Handling raw meat/poultry and then going on to handle cooked meat is particularly dangerous unless you wash your hands thoroughly in between
Avoid touching your nose or coughing or sneezing over food	Many of us carry *Staphylococcus aureus* in our nose and throat which produces a toxin that can cause illness. Don't add your own bacteria to food
Try not to touch food with your hands. Whenever possible use clean tongs to handle food and plates or trays to carry it.	The less your hands are in direct contact with food, the less chance there is of contamination occurring
Avoid touching those parts of dishes or cutlery that come into direct contact with food.	Bacteria on your hands may be transferred to food via the dish or cutlery
Keep your hair covered with a net or hat and do not comb your hair in a food area	Your hair and scalp carry many bacteria that can get into food

Hygiene rules

What should I do?

Why should I do it?

What should I do?	Why should I do it?
Keep finger-nails short and clean and do not wear nail varnish or false nails	Bacteria can collect beneath long nails and get into food you handle. Varnish and false nails can come off in the food
Do not wear jewellery, for example, watches, bracelets, earrings, brooches or rings with stones	Bacteria can collect on items of jewellery or stones or metal may fall into the food. Hand/wrist washing is more thorough if you do not wear a watch or bracelets
Keep cuts, grazes and boils covered with a brightly coloured waterproof dressing – blue is a good colour	Wounds such as these are often infected with bacteria. They must be properly covered to prevent the spread of bacteria. Coloured dressings will be easily spotted if they fall into food
Inform your supervisor if you have: • a stomach upset • cough, cold, or eye or ear discharges • a sore or wound (even if it is covered by a waterproof dressing) • family or close friends who have food-borne illnesses	If you are suffering from any of these conditions you may contaminate food. Often you carry germs before you get symptoms of illness, so you must report food-borne illnesses amongst your close contacts
Wear clean protective over-clothing	Your own clothing may carry bacteria
Do not smoke or eat in a food area	Bringing cigarettes or food to your mouth contaminates your hands. This spreads to food. Also, cigarette ash may fall into food
Keep raw and cooked ready-to-eat foods separate, especially raw meat/poultry and cooked meat/poultry	Raw foods can spread bacteria to other foods that will be eaten without further cooking. Keep raw and cooked ready-to-eat foods apart when handling and storing them

Hygiene rules

What should I do?

Why should I do it?

What should I do?	Why should I do it?
Keep food at the correct temperature during storage and preparation. Remember: • the high risk ready-to-eat foods • the Temperature Danger Zone	High risk ready-to-eat foods (e.g. meat poultry, gravy etc.) provide bacteria with the nutrients and moisture needed to grow. Bacteria multiply at a very fast rate in the Temperature Danger Zone (5°C to 63°C)
Cook food thoroughly so that the centre is heated to a temperature of at least 70°C (82°C in Scotland) for a sufficient length of time and the juices run clear	This is necessary to kill bacteria that may cause illnesses
When food is cooked, serve at once or keep it really hot until it is served, or cool it quickly and refrigerate if it is to be eaten later	To limit the time the food spends in the Temperature Danger Zone and thus prevent the growth of bacteria
Plan ahead: do not prepare food too far in advance or take it out of the refrigerator too soon	To reduce the risk of food being held at temperatures in the Temperature Danger Zone
Make sure that any frozen foods which cannot be cooked from frozen are thoroughly thawed before cooking – especially poultry and large joints of meat	Meat may be cooked on the outside but if it is not completely defrosted the centre of the food may not reach the temperature required to destroy bacteria during cooking
Never re-freeze food after thawing	Bacteria in food will have multiplied during thawing. These bacteria will not be killed by refreezing and they will become active when the raw food is thawed again for a second time

Hygiene rules

What should I do?	Why should I do it?
Keep food covered whenever possible	To protect against contamination
Rotate food stocks – 'first in, first out'. Observe 'Use by' and 'Best before' dates	Using food stocks in the right order reduces the risk of bacteria multiplying and the quality of the food being affected
Always ensure that the workplace is clean before preparing food	Thorough cleaning is necessary to kill any bacteria already present
Only use clean kitchen utensils and equipment and clean them thoroughly, before and after use.	Utensils and equipment may have become contaminated by bacteria which can be transferred to food.
Use clean wiping cloths	Dirty cloths spread bacteria
Never mix different cleaning chemicals	This may make the mixture ineffective and may also produce poisonous gases
'Clean as you go'. Any surfaces or equipment that have been in contact with raw food and any spillages must be cleaned up at once	To avoid the risk of cross-contamination
Put together cleaning schedules for the entire workplace	You will have a list of ALL tasks that must be done, how and by whom, and a timetable for doing them to ensure no area is missed, and hygiene standards are met
Find out about food safety controls in your workplace and carefully follow instructions relating to hazard analysis and safe catering procedures	All food handlers must play their part to reduce the risks of bacterial, chemical and physical hazards contaminating food because they could cause harm to the consumer

More about bacteria

This Appendix provides additional information on some of the bacteria usually associated with food related-illnesses within the United Kingdom. The way in which bacterial growth can be affected by oxygen and acids is also briefly discussed.

Kinds of Bacteria

Salmonella bacteria are found in the gut and excreta of animals and humans. Contamination of food can occur at all points of the food chain - on the farm, in the slaughterhouse or in the kitchen. You can prevent further contamination during food preparation with good hygiene practice and by treating raw meat as infected. Between1987-1993, reported cases of illness due to *Salmonella* increased almost threefold. The main reason for this increase was the well-publicised involvement of poultry and eggs. The organism incriminated was *S. enteritidis* Phage Type 4. Drastic measures to reduce infection rates in flocks of poultry, including the slaughter of 2 million birds produced a downward trend in the reported cases from 2000. There was also a reduction in the proportion of oven-ready chicken infected which at one time was as high as 4 out of 5.

Clostridium perfringens bacteria are found in the gut of animals and humans. The organism is also found in soil. The bacteria produce spores, which may not be killed during cooking or reheating. Meat and poultry are frequently contaminated. Food that is not to be eaten immediately following cooking must be cooled rapidly then refrigerated to prevent the spores turning back into bacteria. The bacteria are a frequent cause of food poisoning.

Staphylococcus aureus bacteria live in our nose and mouth and in cuts and boils. They will multiply rapidly if transferred to foods. The bacteria produce a toxin (poison) that is difficult to destroy with heat. The bacteria can be transferred to food if a food handler has poor standards of personal hygiene. Cooked meats, sandwiches and products containing cream are often contaminated. The bacteria are reported in fewer cases of food poisoning than either *Salmonella* or *Clostridium perfringens*.

Bacillus cereus is particularly associated with rice but can be found in other cereal foods. The bacteria, usually in spore form, are dormant when the food is dry but become active when water is added at cooking. These spores may survive ordinary cooking temperatures. If cooked or partly cooked rice is allowed to 'stand out' at a warm temperature, the bacteria will grow rapidly producing a toxin (poison) that is unlikely to be destroyed even by reheating. Only a small proportion of the total number of reported food poisoning cases have been caused by this bacteria.

Campylobacter jejuni is a major cause of diarrhoea. Since the early 1980s the reported cases of *Campylobacter* infections are more than those for *Salmonella*. Cattle, pigs, poultry, birds and pets carry the bacteria in their gut. The infection spreads in the kitchen by cross-contamination from raw meat to cooked foods. Most cases occur singly; there are few outbreaks where many people are affected. Other sources of infection have been identified. Water supplies have been implicated as has unpasteurised milk and bottled milk which has been pecked by birds.

Listeria monocytogenes is found in the gut of animals and humans, in soil, sewage and throughout the environment. The bacteria can be passed into the milk or gut of animals. Most people have carried the bacteria in their gut at some time. The bacteria usually cause no harm when swallowed, but pregnant women and people with weakened immunity are at risk. The bacteria are unusual in that they can grow in the refrigerator - albeit slowly - at temperatures as low as 3°C. Short storage periods at very low temperatures are essential for all foods associated with *Listeria* - pâtés, cooked chicken, prepared salads and soft cheeses. *Listeria* can cause serious illness, but fortunately the number of reported cases is relatively small.

Escherichia coli (E. coli) is normally found in the gut of people and animals. The bacteria is found anywhere where faecal contamination occurs - on the ground, in sewage, in water and in food prepared by someone with poor personal hygiene. Some types of the bacteria can produce dangerous toxins. *E.coli* O157 is one which can sometimes be harmful to humans, especially to those who are high risk such as elderly people and young children. It is an increasing cause of illness, a large outbreak occurred in Wales in 2006 resulting in 150 cases and the death of a child.

Bacteria and Oxygen

Some bacteria require the presence of oxygen to grow: these are classified as 'aerobic'. Others that will not grow if oxygen is present are classified as 'anaerobic'. There are also bacteria that can tolerate either condition. Sometimes it is possible to deny bacteria the environment they favour. For example, the risk from aerobic-type bacteria can be reduced by vacuum packing, i.e. the air is extracted from the wrapper containing the food - but remember it still needs refrigeration.

Bacteria and acids

Bacteria do not like acid and if enough is present in food they will not grow. The extent to which foods are acidic is measured on the 'pH' scale. A measurement of pH 7.0 denotes that a food is 'neutral'; bacteria grow best in neutral foods. Measurements lower than pH 7.0 indicate that acid is present; the lower the figure, the more acid there is in the food. Foods measuring pH 3.7 or lower are known as 'high acid' foods and bacteria do not find such foods suitable for their growth. Chicken (pH 6.3) is an example of a near neutral food, whereas grapefruit (pH 3.0) is one of the high acid foods that provide little scope for bacteria to grow.

Infectivity

The risk of becoming ill after eating contaminated food varies and depends on:

- the type of person - you already know the groups of people who are considered at risk.

- the type of bacteria - most food poisoning bacteria need large numbers to overcome the body's defences such as stomach acid. However, *Campylobacter* and toxin-producing *E.coli* are exceptions where symptoms arise from smaller doses. *E.coli* bacteria are resistant to acids.

- the type of food - some fatty foods can protect bacteria from stomach acid so small numbers may be enough to cause illness. *Salmonella* in chocolate is an example.

Index

Index